THE LIFE PASSION JOURNAL

102 Powerful Prompts to Crush Self-Doubt and Unlock a Remarkable Life

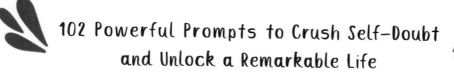

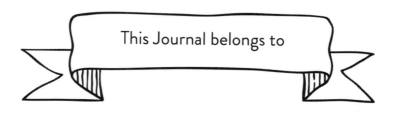

This Journal belongs to

_____

Copyright 2018 by Barrie Davenport.
Bold Living Press

ISBN-13: 978-1-7320350-1-0

DISCLAIMER

A Gift for You

As a way of saying thank you for purchasing this journal, I hope you'll enjoy my free eBook, "The Life Passion Mindset: 6 Lies Keeping You from the Life You Deserve." Just copy and paste this URL into your browser: passionj.co

About Barrie Davenport

Barrie Davenport is a certified personal coach, thought leader, best-selling author, and creator of several online courses, including The Path to Passion Course. She is the founder of the top-ranked personal development site, Live Bold and Bloom. com.

Her work as a coach, blogger, and author is focused on offering people practical strategies for living happier, more successful, and more mindful lives. She utilizes time-tested, evidence-based, action-oriented principles and methods to create real and measurable results for self-improvement.

You can learn more about Barrie on her Amazon author page at barriedavenport.com/author.

The Power of Passion

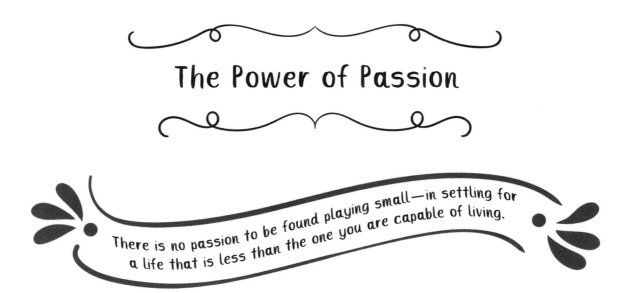

There is no passion to be found playing small—in settling for a life that is less than the one you are capable of living.

Nelson Mandela

Too many people in the world are living lives of quiet desperation. They get up, go to a job they don't like, come home and watch a few hours of TV, go to bed, and do it all over again the next day. That's not a life.

Some of us have lives less desperate than this, but still we feel empty and unhappy too often. Maybe we have times of happiness and fun, but mostly we think about the life we wish we were living—even though we don't quite know what that would look like.

I firmly believe there are deep wells of interest and passion inside many of us (most of us) that have never been tapped, because we've never been exposed to them in our day-to-day lives—or because we were prevented (by well-meaning parents, teachers, advisors, or our own misperceptions) from exploring these deep wells.

We find ourselves living life on autopilot, even though we are bored, unhappy, and longing for more. The years go by and we keep traveling down the same uninspiring road, only to feel increasingly stuck and confused.

Even when opportunities for change come our way, we aren't sure whether or not to take them. How do you even begin uncovering your passion when you feel so paralyzed? Finding and living your life passion involves far more than a career you can tolerate, a hobby that's entertaining, or volunteer work that's fulfilling.

It's a mindset and a lifestyle, one that's imbued with energy, excitement, and enthusiasm and powered by a passion pursuit. That pursuit may be a career or avocation or something else entirely. But whatever it is, it colors the entirety of your life for the better.

Pursuing it requires a total mind shift to change the way you think about yourself and how you operate in the world—so that you prioritize living passionately ahead of living predictably. You see a passionate life as the only way you want to live, and you begin making choices accordingly.

Does that mean you have to give up your job and start over with everything? Maybe, but not necessarily. You get to be the creator of your passionate life based on your desires and priorities. You decide what you are willing to sacrifice or compromise, and what's worth testing and pursuing based on your particular dreams for a passionate life.

When you decide a passionate life is a goal worth pursuing, the details are more manageable than you might think. It may not be an overnight process, but the power of your passion helps you clarify the way to make it happen.

You'll find solutions and overcome roadblocks that previously seemed insurmountable. Enthusiasm breeds creativity, energy, and motivation.

Sadly, most people don't get this far. They don't get past the first roadblock when they ponder finding their passion and speculate on what it might take to make it real. It all feels scary and overwhelming, so they turn around and scurry back to the status quo before they even discover what lights their fire.

They don't see living more passionately as a goal worth pursuing because they aren't clear on the result—what a passionate life looks like. Of course, the specifics differ for everyone, but there are some consistent qualities of a passionate life that everyone can enjoy.

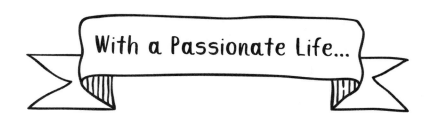

With a Passionate Life...

You have a general sense of energy, enthusiasm, and purpose.

You feel deeply engaged in your passionate pursuit(s).

That engagement and the joy it brings spills over into other areas of your life, enhancing your general outlook and self-confidence.

You are compelled to simplify your life because you want to spend more time doing what you love.

Problems and life difficulties diminish because you are happier and have fewer complications.

You have better relationships because you are more attractive, positive, and interesting.

You frequently experience the sense of being "in the flow," when time disappears and you have a deep sense of satisfaction in your passion.

Even when you aren't proficient at your passion pursuit, you enjoy the practice of it and the process of learning.

With the promise of these positive outcomes, you may still have reservations about what might happen and where it will all lead. It's daunting to challenge the status quo and think about disrupting your life for something that may or may not work out for the better.

You may underestimate yourself and have limiting beliefs that you don't have what it takes to change your life situation. You may have legitimate fears about your financial security for yourself and your family.

You might believe you don't have the time or patience to work on figuring it all out. You might even believe you don't have a passion, so all of the efforts would be a big waste of time.

I'd like to ask you to suspend any fears, limiting beliefs, and perceived roadblocks as you work through this journal.

Embrace the idea that you are beginning an adventure that will lead you to more self-awareness, clarity, and motivation. That's all you need to do for now. Once you make the decision to uncover your passion by working on this journal, you'll find that the process offers so much satisfaction on its own.

You know a positive outcome is ahead, so the work to reach that outcome doesn't really feel like work. Your passion isn't just a destination—it's a journey. Enjoy the steps involved in uncovering it. View this journaling process as your passion for right now.

As part of this adventure, you'll enjoy many other benefits, in addition to uncovering what ignites your enthusiasm with passion and purpose.

1. You'll learn more about yourself.

The first step always involves some self-discovery work, which is fascinating and enlightening. You'll learn more about your personality type, aptitudes, and strong interests.

You'll also uncover what holds you back, the internal roadblocks that keep you from living the life you dream of and how you can overcome those roadblocks.

2. You'll get clear on your values and life priorities.

You'll define the core principles for your life, in addition to the areas of your life that are the most important to you, which will help you create the framework for making decisions about your passion.

Your passion should align with your values for it to fit comfortably into your life and for you to feel you're living authentically.

3. You'll stretch yourself.

Searching for your passion requires stepping out of your comfort zone. You need to remain open to opportunities and possibilities you may not have considered previously. You may need to take action in ways that don't feel entirely comfortable.

All of these feel risky and scary at first, but as you begin to take small actions to follow your dream, you'll discover it's all more manageable than you feared. This gives you a sense of pride and confidence.

4. You'll realize the value of experimentation.

We generally don't know what we're passionate about until we're immersed in an endeavor and experience the daily actions involved in it. That's why experimentation is so valuable.

It does take time, and you may discover the pursuit you're testing is not for you after all. But you won't come away empty-handed. You'll gain more clarity about your passion, and you'll encounter new people, experiences, and insights to help you.

5. You'll find joy in the process.

You don't have to delay happiness until you find your passion. You can be happy during the process of finding it. This is where a positive attitude comes in.

Everything you learn about yourself, every experiment you undertake can be exciting and build anticipation. Working toward something important is deeply satisfying.

6. You'll meet new, like-minded people.

One of the benefits of seeking a passionate life is discovering other passionate people along the way. Once you tell people you're working on this journal to uncover your passion, you'll be amazed at how many people appear to support you.

If they don't appear, you can go find them in Meetups, forums, Facebook groups, and networking organizations. Don't be shy about talking about your search and meeting up with people who seem to be deeply engaged and passionate about what they are doing.

7. You'll simplify your life.

When we feel bored, unhappy, and confused, we tend to overcomplicate our lives and fill the void with material things, busy work, and distractions. Once you find something you feel passionate about, you don't have the time or inclination for those things any longer.

You become so engaged and excited about what you're doing that you don't want clutter and trifles to interfere with your passion. You streamline your life to those priorities you identified earlier and rid yourself of the extraneous.

8. You'll improve your emotional and mental health.

The process of searching for your passion gives you hope, excitement, and energy. It provides focus and distraction from your day-to-day worries and frustrations.

When you feel you have control over your own destiny, and you take action to create your life rather than just react to it, you relieve the feelings of frustration, depression, and hopelessness you may have felt.

> 9. You'll discover more meaning. <

So much dissatisfaction in life comes from the feeling of meaninglessness. You may question, "Why am I here? What value does my life or my work bring to the world?"

Seeking your life passion often leads to finding a purpose in your life. You may well discover that what you feel passionate about also gives you a sense of inner fulfillment and meaning.

> 10. You'll gain more confidence. <

Having the clarity that this journaling process provides will give you a huge boost in your confidence. You won't feel confused or directionless. You'll know what you want and feel inspired and motivated to go after it.

Clarity and confidence help you make sound, well-considered decisions about the steps you should take to make your passion a reality.

You might wonder if this journal on finding your passion can help you live your passion in day-to-day life. Don't worry—at the end of the journal, I'll give you ideas and strategies for proceeding with the information you've discovered related to your passion, so you can figure out how to take action and apply it to your life.

HOW TO USE THIS JOURNAL

The purpose of this journal is to help you (1) uncover what you might feel passionate about, (2) know how to narrow your search and refine your ideas, (3) address real and perceived roadblocks, and (4) transition from the life you have now to a more passionate life.

Every person working through this journal has different life responsibilities, family obligations, financial situations, and risk tolerance. There isn't a "one size fits all" solution that works for everyone.

But there is a consistent path that leads everyone to the right doorway. It will be your job to open the door and take the necessary actions for change.

You can work through this journal at your own pace, but try to work on it at least weekly to keep the momentum going. You may find yourself revisiting questions and prompts as you've had more time to think and adjust your responses.

You'll find these questions provoke deep levels of awareness over time, and certain answers might arise days or even weeks after you first explore the question.

It is amazing how acknowledging the truth of who you are and what you want will motivate and inspire you toward creative ideas and forward-moving action toward finding your passion.

Understanding the truth about what you want for your life and how you might be holding yourself back is the first step. But knowledge without action is useless.

If you want to find your passion, you need to take action on what you've learned. Without knowing your specific answers, it's hard to tell you exactly what actions to take, but I can give you some insights into figuring it out for yourself.

Pay attention to what you enjoy

As you answer the questions, look for patterns and related activities, job responsibilities, and hobbies that historically have been positive for you.
These are clues about what your passion might involve or what it could be.

You may not see patterns immediately, but as you explore ideas, revisit these favorite activities to ensure they are part of any job or endeavor you are considering.

When I went through my own passion search, one the positive activities I listed was helping my friends with their problems. I didn't immediately see this interest as having the potential for a life passion, but as I began researching the life coaching profession, I saw how this favorite activity fit perfectly with the career.

Don't toss out anything you enjoy because you assume it doesn't have career or passion potential. It's too early in the game to assume that yet.

Pay attention to what you hate

If you're miserable or bored with any aspect of your work or life, you'll feel unhappy with your entire life. One really negative situation, person, or mindset can infect everything.

Finding your passion is as much about excising what you don't like about your life as it is about finding what you love. You have to make room for your passion by getting rid of the dead weight.

Challenge your assumptions constantly

One of the reasons we get so stuck in a passion search is that we tend to believe everything we think. "I can't afford to quit my job." "Everyone will think I'm crazy if I do this." "I'll never be able to make the money I'm making now." "If I make the wrong decision, it will ruin my life."

Most of your assumptions are either completely untrue or only partially true. Most of the challenges you'll face when pursuing your passion are figure-out-able.

Rather than beginning the process with a foundation of fear, begin with an assumption of success. Say to yourself, "I am determined to find my life passion and arrange my life so that I can live it every day."

Of course, you'll have to make uncomfortable decisions and life changes. You may have to let go of something good to get to something great. But if you accept that as part of the process, and keep your eye on the prize, all the scary parts won't feel so scary.

➤ Never contradict your core values ➤

Defining your core values will be part of this journaling process. You'll learn what your life principles are and what you value most. Try not to make any big decisions or life changes that contradict those values.

For example, if one of your primary values is family time, and you're offered an amazing job doing something you love that requires you to travel five days a week, you'll eventually feel conflicted and unhappy.

If one of your values is personal integrity, but you know your boss has done some questionable things, then you'll feel resentful and icky. Prioritize your values, and you can't go wrong.

➤ Be willing to invest time and money ➤

We'd all just love it if our life passion showed up at the doorstep and fit in seamlessly with our current lives. But if it were that easy, everyone would be living passionate lives.

- You may have to go back to school or get more training for your passion.
- You may have to take a side gig for a while to earn extra money.
- You might need to offer your services for free in your passion interest to make sure you really like it.
- You may need to tighten the belt to save money to start a business.
- You might have to let go of prestige and power to follow your passion.

Before I had children, if someone said to me, "You will feel extremely nauseated for four months, gain 40 pounds, have swollen ankles, get stretch marks, suffer from sciatica and insomnia, not be able to tie your own shoes, and go through 48 hours of intense contractions followed by pushing out a 9-pound human," I would have felt a bit reticent to take on the challenge.

Of course, I knew these things before having children. And I'm sure my fears were far out-of-proportion to the reality. But I also knew that the end result would be amazing and life-changing. My pain was short-lived, but my happiness with my kids was a lifelong reward.

More than likely, some amount of short-term sacrifice and discomfort will be required of you. But in the grand scheme of things, this discomfort is nothing compared to the joy of the new life you are creating, which can last a lifetime.

Answering the Questions

As you read the questions in the following sections, speak each question out loud, as though you are your own coach. Then close your eyes and allow the answers to rise to the surface of your consciousness. Write down your thoughts quickly, in bullet points if possible, so you can continue to focus on the answers that are coming up for you.

Don't stop with the first few answers you come up with. After every answer you write down, ask yourself, "Is there more?" Keep asking this until you have nothing left to add.

Some of your own answers may feel uncomfortable, scary, or even contradictory to the life or work you think you should pursue. We all have preconceived, entrenched beliefs about what we can and can't do. We are held back by the opinions of others and the fear of the unknown.

Try not to allow those beliefs and fears to get in the way of your authentic, honest answers. Be real with yourself, because you can't find your passion if you're using a broken compass to guide the way.

If you get stuck on a question and don't have an answer, just skip it for now. Sometimes the answer will come to you when you sit on it for a while.

One last thing—try to enjoy this journaling process. This could be the beginning of an extraordinary journey for you. It's exciting to really get to know yourself and to give yourself permission to extricate all the hidden dreams and desires you may never have recognized before.

Begin with a mindset of positive expectation and curiosity to get the most from these questions.

Note: If you need more space to answer any of the questions, you'll find additional blank pages at the end of the journal.

By becoming
SELF-AWARE,
you gain ownership
of REALITY;

in becoming REAL,
you become the
master of both inner
and outer LIFE.

DEEPAK CHOPRA

· ☆ ·

1. What is your personality type? *(You can take a free online version of the Jung Typology Test/Myers-Briggs Type Indicator assessment at humanmetrics.com.)* Do some online research about your four-letter type. What resonates with you about your innate preferences? What doesn't seem like you? Be as detailed as possible.

_____

_____

_____

_____

_____

_____

_____

_____

_____

_____

_____

_____

_____

· ·

2. How do your current work and lifestyle complement or support your innate personality preferences? How are you not supporting or complementing your personality preferences with your work or lifestyle?

_____

_____

_____

_____

_____

_____

_____

_____

_____

_____

_____

_____

_____

· ☆ ·

3. Read online about the theory of "multiple intelligences" developed by Dr. Howard Gardner, and take an online, multiple intelligence test. *(Go to edutopia. org/multiple-intelligences-assessment.)* How do your work and lifestyle support your natural intelligence type(s)? How are you not supporting your intelligence type(s) in your work or lifestyle?

_____

_____

_____

_____

_____

_____

_____

_____

_____

_____

_____

· ·

4. What are your skills and aptitudes related to your work, hobbies, relationships, creative abilities, physical abilities, cognitive abilities, and communication? *(Refer to the Skills Inventory list at the end of the journal.)* List as many as you can think of, even if they seem insignificant.

_____

_____

_____

_____

_____

_____

_____

_____

_____

_____

_____

_____

_____

_____

_____

5. Of the skills and aptitudes you listed, which bring you the most pleasure and fulfillment? Which would you like to learn or pursue more? Which would you like to avoid if you could?

_____

_____

_____

_____

_____

_____

_____

_____

_____

_____

_____

_____

_____

6. What are your top five core values in your personal life? What are your top five core values in your professional life? *(Refer to the 400 Value Words list at the end of the journal.)*

_____

_____

_____

_____

_____

_____

_____

_____

_____

_____

_____

_____

_____

_____

7. How do your work and personal life currently support these values? How are you acting against your values in your personal or professional life?

_____

_____

_____

_____

_____

_____

_____

_____

_____

_____

_____

_____

_____

_____

8. What would need to change in your life or work to align more closely with your values? Be as specific as possible.

_____

_____

_____

_____

_____

_____

_____

_____

_____

_____

_____

_____

_____

_____

9. What are some childhood dreams or interests you were never able to fully explore but still find intriguing? What activities, work, and projects have brought you joy and fulfillment in the past?

_____

_____

_____

_____

_____

_____

_____

_____

_____

_____

_____

_____

_____

_____

10. If you could be remembered for three things after you die, what would they be?

_____

_____

_____

_____

_____

_____

_____

_____

_____

_____

_____

_____

_____

_____

11. Who is someone in your life, a public figure or someone from history, whose life and work inspires and excites you? Why?

_____

_____

_____

_____

_____

_____

_____

_____

_____

_____

_____

_____

_____

_____

_____

☆

12. What is working well for you in your current life and career? What do you find fulfilling, meaningful, enjoyable, and important?

_____

_____

_____

_____

_____

_____

_____

_____

_____

_____

_____

_____

_____

_____

_____

13. What isn't working well for you in your current life and career? What drains you, makes you stressed and anxious, or wastes your time?

· ☆ ·

14. If you were financially secure and didn't need a paycheck, how would you spend your time?

_____

_____

_____

_____

_____

_____

_____

_____

_____

_____

_____

_____

_____

_____

· ·

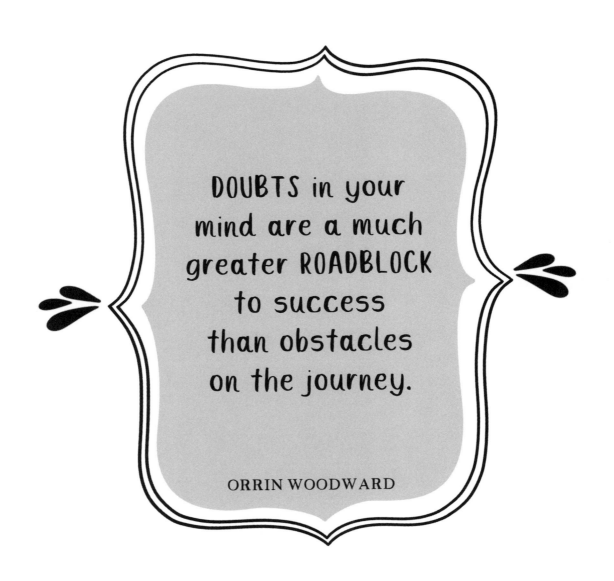

DOUBTS in your mind are a much greater ROADBLOCK to success than obstacles on the journey.

ORRIN WOODWARD

15. How are you living outside of your integrity? What needs to change?

_____

_____

_____

_____

_____

_____

_____

_____

_____

_____

_____

_____

_____

_____

_____

_____

16. What lies are you telling yourself and others about who you are and what's important to you? How can you be more authentic with yourself and others?

_____

_____

_____

_____

_____

_____

_____

_____

_____

_____

_____

_____

_____

_____

_____

_____

_____

17. What are the time-wasting, frustrating activities or behaviors in your personal life and at work that you would like to diminish or to eliminate completely?

_____

_____

_____

_____

_____

_____

_____

_____

_____

_____

_____

_____

_____

_____

18. Why have you allowed these time wasters and frustrations to infect your life? How are they "fillers" to prevent you from pursuing your passion?

_____

_____

_____

_____

_____

_____

_____

_____

_____

_____

_____

_____

_____

_____

_____

19. What do you fear most when it comes to finding your passion? What is the linchpin fear preventing you from going after your passion?

_____

_____

_____

_____

_____

_____

_____

_____

_____

_____

_____

_____

_____

20. What limiting beliefs do you hold about yourself and your ability to succeed at making your passion part of your life?

_____

_____

_____

_____

_____

_____

_____

_____

_____

_____

_____

_____

_____

_____

_____

_____

21. How have your fears and limiting beliefs held you back from finding or pursuing your passion in the past?

_____

_____

_____

_____

_____

_____

_____

_____

_____

_____

_____

_____

_____

_____

22. What solid evidence do you have that your fears and limiting beliefs are true?

_____

_____

_____

_____

_____

_____

_____

_____

_____

_____

_____

_____

_____

_____

_____

23. If there's some small amount of evidence that your fears or limiting beliefs might happen, is the risk big enough to prevent you from going after your passion?

_____

_____

_____

_____

_____

_____

_____

_____

_____

_____

_____

_____

_____

24. Can you tolerate some risk and uncertainty about finding your passion? How much?

_____

_____

_____

_____

_____

_____

_____

_____

_____

_____

_____

_____

_____

_____

25. What trumps finding and living your passion? Your current income? Your job? Your current lifestyle? Your home or the city you live in? The opinions of others? How you spend your time? Something else?

_____

_____

_____

_____

_____

_____

_____

_____

_____

_____

_____

_____

_____

26. Specifically, what actions can you take to lessen and manage your fear?

_____

_____

_____

_____

_____

_____

_____

_____

_____

_____

_____

_____

_____

_____

_____

· ☆ ·

27. Are there any people in your life preventing you from pursuing your passion? Who are they and how are they holding you back?

_____

_____

_____

_____

_____

_____

_____

_____

_____

_____

_____

_____

_____

· ·

28. What could you do to communicate with these people (*person*) to enlist their support or get them to step out of your way?

_____

_____

_____

_____

_____

_____

_____

_____

_____

_____

_____

_____

_____

_____

_____

29. Are you willing to disengage entirely from people who are undermining your passion pursuit? If not, why?

_____

_____

_____

_____

_____

_____

_____

_____

_____

_____

_____

_____

_____

_____

_____

_____

30. Do any people close to you have legitimate concerns or worries about your passion ideas? How can you address or overcome these?

_____

_____

_____

_____

_____

_____

_____

_____

_____

_____

_____

_____

_____

_____

_____

31. Are you dealing with any unresolved emotional issues, mental health challenges, illnesses, or anything else that could hinder you from pursuing your passion? If so, what can you do to address these issues to free you to work on your passion?

_____

_____

_____

_____

_____

_____

_____

_____

_____

_____

_____

_____

_____

32. How is your life currently out-of-balance, over-scheduled, cluttered, or over-complicated in your physical space, your material things, your lifestyle, and your frame of mind?

_____

_____

_____

_____

_____

_____

_____

_____

_____

_____

_____

_____

_____

_____

33. What specific actions can you take to restore more balance, space, and simplicity to your life to make room for your life passion when you find it?

_____

_____

_____

_____

_____

_____

_____

_____

_____

_____

_____

_____

_____

_____

34. What do you keep tolerating from other people or yourself, at work and in your personal life, that drains your energy and makes you feel "lesser than"? What would happen if you stopped tolerating these things?

_____

_____

_____

_____

_____

_____

_____

_____

_____

_____

_____

_____

_____

Our PASSIONS are the winds that propel our vessel. Our reason is the pilot that steers her. Without WINDS the vessel would not move and without a PILOT she would be lost.

PROVERB

35. What kind of physical work environment do you prefer and allows you to be most productive? Be detailed and specific.

_____

_____

_____

_____

_____

_____

_____

_____

_____

_____

_____

_____

_____

_____

_____

36. Do you prefer to be an employee or your own supervisor? Write down specifically why you prefer one or the other.

_____

_____

_____

_____

_____

_____

_____

_____

_____

_____

_____

_____

_____

_____

_____

_____

37. How much do you want to interact with other people as part of your work? How much would you prefer to work alone?

_____

_____

_____

_____

_____

_____

_____

_____

_____

_____

_____

_____

_____

_____

38. What satisfaction do you seek in a profession that you haven't found in your current position/career?

_____

_____

_____

_____

_____

_____

_____

_____

_____

_____

_____

_____

_____

_____

39. If certain things changed, could you feel passionate about your current career/job? What would those things be? How could you make those changes, if possible?

_____

_____

_____

_____

_____

_____

_____

_____

_____

_____

_____

_____

_____

_____

_____

_____

40. What do you most need from an employer or supervisor to feel valued and respected?

_____

_____

_____

_____

_____

_____

_____

_____

_____

_____

_____

_____

_____

_____

_____

41. If you had to make the decision today to stay with your job or pursue another one *(with a guarantee of employment, the same salary, and benefits)*, would you leave your current job? Why or why not?

_____

_____

_____

_____

_____

_____

_____

_____

_____

_____

_____

_____

_____

_____

42. Do you have enough savings to allow you to live for six months during a job transition or while you search for your passion? If not, how can you start saving or earning more to create this buffer?

_____

_____

_____

_____

_____

_____

_____

_____

_____

_____

_____

_____

_____

43. What is the minimum salary you can live with?

44. Would you be willing to downsize your lifestyle to live your passion? If you have a spouse or partner, would he or she support that?

_____

_____

_____

_____

_____

_____

_____

_____

_____

_____

_____

_____

_____

_____

_____

45. What is the worst thing that could happen if you decided to pursue your passion? Could you live with that?

_____

_____

_____

_____

_____

_____

_____

_____

_____

_____

_____

_____

_____

_____

46. What is the actual likelihood of this worst thing happening?

_____

_____

_____

_____

_____

_____

_____

_____

_____

_____

_____

_____

_____

_____

47. If you absolutely cannot afford to leave your job right now, how much time could you devote to a passion outside of work?

_____

_____

_____

_____

_____

_____

_____

_____

_____

_____

_____

_____

_____

_____

48. What kind of additional education, training, or skills might you need for a potential career change or passionate pursuit? Write down any possibilities that come to mind.

_____

_____

_____

_____

_____

_____

_____

_____

_____

_____

_____

_____

_____

_____

49. How much money and time will additional education or training take? Where will you get the money and how can you carve out the time? Be creative.

_____

_____

_____

_____

_____

_____

_____

_____

_____

_____

_____

_____

_____

_____

50. Who will be affected by a career change if you make one? How will the career change impact your personal life and relationships? What might you need to do to address any negative impact?

_____

_____

_____

_____

_____

_____

_____

_____

_____

_____

_____

_____

_____

_____

51. Could you accept a pay cut or a less prestigious position if you are more passionate and fulfilled by the work you are doing?

_____

_____

_____

_____

_____

_____

_____

_____

_____

_____

_____

_____

_____

_____

_____

52. If you found passionate work, but it didn't pay you enough, would you be willing to take on a side-hustle to make ends meet or create savings?

_____

_____

_____

_____

_____

_____

_____

_____

_____

_____

_____

_____

_____

_____

_____

53. Who do you know who is doing something that you find interesting, exciting, and engaging? What is it that intrigues you about what he or she is doing?

_____

_____

_____

_____

_____

_____

_____

_____

_____

_____

_____

_____

_____

_____

_____

54. What person or people can you go to for feedback, ideas, support, and direction about what you are best suited to do and how to make it happen? Who could be a possible mentor for you?

_____

_____

_____

_____

_____

_____

_____

_____

_____

_____

_____

_____

_____

_____

55. What kind of people do you consider to be your tribe? What are their interests, values, workstyles, hobbies, and goals?

_____

_____

_____

_____

_____

_____

_____

_____

_____

_____

_____

_____

_____

_____

_____

56. How important is it for you to have a job that feels meaningful and purposeful? What does that mean specifically to you?

_____

_____

_____

_____

_____

_____

_____

_____

_____

_____

_____

_____

_____

_____

_____

_____

57. How much freedom and flexibility do you want in a job? Be specific.

_____

_____

_____

_____

_____

_____

_____

_____

_____

_____

_____

_____

_____

58. How important is it for you to have benefits and perks with your job? What kind do you absolutely need? What can you live without if you are happy with the work?

_____

_____

_____

_____

_____

_____

_____

_____

_____

_____

_____

_____

_____

59. What motivates you the most when it comes to your profession—money, prestige, respect, fulfillment, purpose, creativity, intellectual stimulation, or something else? Be specific about everything that motivates you and excites you to want to work. If it's several of these, prioritize them.

_____

_____

_____

_____

_____

_____

_____

_____

_____

_____

_____

_____

_____

_____

60. Does your home and the décor/furnishings generally reflect who you are and how you wish to live? If not, what would you change?

_____

_____

_____

_____

_____

_____

_____

_____

_____

_____

_____

_____

_____

_____

_____

_____

61. Do you feel comfortable and happy in your home? List the ways you do and don't feel comfortable and happy.

_____

_____

_____

_____

_____

_____

_____

_____

_____

_____

_____

_____

_____

_____

62. Are you living in the right city for you and your family? Are the climate, culture, and amenities ideal? If not, where would you rather live and why?

63. Does your neighborhood or community reflect your values and provide adequate entertainment, services, and amenities? Do you connect with the people around you?

_____

_____

_____

_____

_____

_____

_____

_____

_____

_____

_____

_____

_____

_____

64. What could you change about your home, community, or the city in which you live that would align with your values and make your life better or happier?

_____

_____

_____

_____

_____

_____

_____

_____

_____

_____

_____

_____

_____

_____

65. How do you spend the vast majority of your time outside of work? Are there any activities that you could eliminate, delegate, or hire out to someone else? What are they?

_____

_____

_____

_____

_____

_____

_____

_____

_____

_____

_____

_____

_____

The heart of human excellence often begins to beat when you DISCOVER a pursuit that absorbs you, frees you, challenges you, or gives you a sense of meaning, joy, or PASSION.

TERRY ORLICK

66. What interests or hobbies have you had in the past few years that intrigue you and might hold potential for a life passion?

_____

_____

_____

_____

_____

_____

_____

_____

_____

_____

_____

_____

_____

_____

67. What would your ideal day look like? Describe it in detail from morning until bedtime.

_____

_____

_____

_____

_____

_____

_____

_____

_____

_____

_____

_____

_____

_____

68. What is something (*or several things*) you'd really like to achieve before you die? What have you done toward making these happen?

_____

_____

_____

_____

_____

_____

_____

_____

_____

_____

_____

_____

_____

_____

_____

69. What would make you feel proud of yourself?

70. If you could start fresh all over again with your life and career, what would you do differently? Can you go back for a "redo" on any of these things? If you answer "no," are you absolutely sure?

_____

_____

_____

_____

_____

_____

_____

_____

_____

_____

_____

_____

_____

_____

71. Do you have any professional goals defined? Short-term? Long-term?
What are they?

72. In what ways are you not living up to your potential? What could you do to change that?

_____

_____

_____

_____

_____

_____

_____

_____

_____

_____

_____

_____

_____

_____

73. Do you feel there is *(or should be)* a purpose for your life and/or work? If so, what do you believe this purpose is and how can you best express it in your life?

74. Of all the interests and activities in your personal life and professional life, which do you find the most engaging and enjoyable? These can be mundane actions, like helping a child with homework, or something more substantial, like being a project manager. List as many as you can think of.

_____

_____

_____

_____

_____

_____

_____

_____

_____

_____

_____

_____

_____

75. Of the interests you listed above, do any seem to connect or relate to one another? Is there a combination of interests that could potentially be part of a career or business? If so, detail your ideas.

_____

_____

_____

_____

_____

_____

_____

_____

_____

_____

_____

_____

_____

76. Looking back at your answers related to your interests, values, career preferences, lifestyle preferences, write a rough draft vision for a passionate life that includes your work, relationships, hobbies, lifestyle, social life, home environment, and anything else you want to include.

_____

_____

_____

_____

_____

_____

_____

_____

_____

_____

_____

_____

_____

_____

_____

77. Take a look at your current life to see how much of it matches the vision you just wrote. You want to hang on to those things and remember that part of your vision is already happening. Where does your life now match your vision?

_____

_____

_____

_____

_____

_____

_____

_____

_____

_____

_____

_____

_____

78. Brainstorm some ways you can bring in extra cash in a pinch. What could you do on the side or as a consultant? How much could you make?

_____

_____

_____

_____

_____

_____

_____

_____

_____

_____

_____

_____

_____

_____

79. What careers and hobbies are typical for your personality and intelligence type? *(You can research your type to learn more.)* Which of these careers and hobbies are particularly interesting to you and why?

_____

_____

_____

_____

_____

_____

_____

_____

_____

_____

_____

_____

_____

_____

80. How would living out your vision for a passionate life impact you physically, mentally, emotionally, in your relationships, and in your self-confidence?

_____

_____

_____

_____

_____

_____

_____

_____

_____

_____

_____

_____

_____

_____

_____

81. Take a moment to close your eyes and visualize yourself living a life that is exciting, engaging, fulfilling, financially secure, meaningful, and passionate. Imagine waking up every day with a positive, enthusiastic mindset. How does this visualization make you feel?

_____

_____

_____

_____

_____

_____

_____

_____

_____

_____

_____

_____

_____

_____

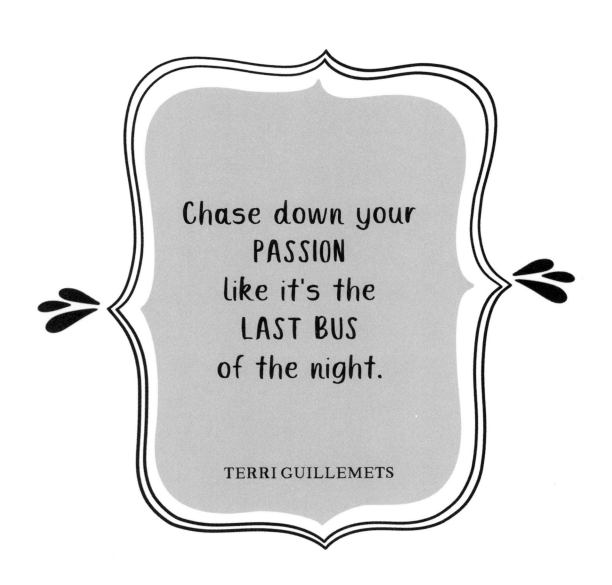

Chase down your
PASSION
like it's the
LAST BUS
of the night.

TERRI GUILLEMETS

82. Based on all you have learned about yourself so far, write a list of the top five to ten ideas you have for your life passion. Don't worry if some of them don't seem realistic now; just write down the ideas.

---

83. What research and reading are involved in learning more about these pursuits? List everything you can think of to feel you have a solid knowledge of what it takes to make these pursuits happen and/or to become proficient at them.

_____

_____

_____

_____

_____

_____

_____

_____

_____

_____

_____

_____

_____

_____

84. Brainstorm and list any other small actions you should take to begin pursuing the interests or possible passions, like talking to a friend or mentor, updating your résumé, learning about salary and growth potential, etc.

_____

_____

_____

_____

_____

_____

_____

_____

_____

_____

_____

_____

_____

85. In the short term, how do you best see yourself pursuing your passion—in your career, a hobby, a side-gig, or something else? What about the long-term?

_____

_____

_____

_____

_____

_____

_____

_____

_____

_____

_____

_____

_____

_____

_____

_____

86. If you can't change careers in the short term, how much time can you devote to a passionate hobby or side-gig?

_____

_____

_____

_____

_____

_____

_____

_____

_____

_____

_____

_____

_____

_____

87. If you decide to pursue your passion in your career, what are some specific actions you need to take to prepare for changing jobs or careers?

_____

_____

_____

_____

_____

_____

_____

_____

_____

_____

_____

_____

_____

_____

_____

_____

88. What are some of the potential challenges you might face in changing careers and what can you do to mitigate those challenges?

_____

_____

_____

_____

_____

_____

_____

_____

_____

_____

_____

_____

_____

_____

89. Before you consider leaving your current job, what are possible options with your employer that might satisfy your passion, such as a different position, more flexible hours, a different supervisor, or working from home? Are any of these realistic and if so, what can you do to initiate them?

_____

_____

_____

_____

_____

_____

_____

_____

_____

_____

_____

_____

90. How can you experiment with your possible passions by volunteering, shadowing someone, taking on a contract or part-time job to test it, enrolling in an introduction class, or otherwise committing to some short-term exposure that doesn't require a full commitment?

_____

_____

_____

_____

_____

_____

_____

_____

_____

_____

_____

_____

_____

_____

91. How much time are you willing to invest in experimenting before making a decision? How will you know if something feels right? How will you know if it feels wrong?

_____

_____

_____

_____

_____

_____

_____

_____

_____

_____

_____

_____

_____

_____

92. Who could you contact that is already an expert at your possible passion pursuits to ask questions and learn more about the day-to-day reality of this pursuit?

_____

_____

_____

_____

_____

_____

_____

_____

_____

_____

_____

_____

_____

93. What kind of feelers could you put out about your interests and possible career change without jeopardizing your current job?

_____

_____

_____

_____

_____

_____

_____

_____

_____

_____

_____

_____

_____

_____

94. Do any of your passion possibilities involve becoming more proficient in a specific skill set? If so, specifically what needs to be done to practice or learn the skill set? How much time are you willing to devote to practice and/or learning?

_____

_____

_____

_____

_____

_____

_____

_____

_____

_____

_____

_____

_____

95. Which of your passion possibilities seem to fit best with your values, desired lifestyle, relationships, financial goals and obligations, and other practical life considerations?

_____

_____

_____

_____

_____

_____

_____

_____

_____

_____

_____

_____

_____

96. Are there any changes or actions you need to take to address emotional, physical, or relationship issues that might get in the way of pursuing your passion? If so, what are the changes or actions and what is your plan for dealing with them?

_____

_____

_____

_____

_____

_____

_____

_____

_____

_____

_____

_____

_____

97. How much time a week are you willing to invest in following through on some of the research, experimentation, and action steps you have defined in the previous questions? Specifically, what days and times can you carve out for this?

98. What kind of accountability system can you create to help you stay on track with your weekly life passion action steps? This could be another person, a forum, social media, or working with a coach or mentor.

_____

_____

_____

_____

_____

_____

_____

_____

_____

_____

_____

_____

_____

_____

99. Now that you've come this far with your journal, do you have more clarity about the passion you want to pursue and how you want to apply it to your life? What do you believe is the best direction to take at this point?

_____

_____

_____

_____

_____

_____

_____

_____

_____

_____

_____

_____

_____

100. What concerns, fears, or limiting beliefs do you still have about making a change in your life to include your passion? What more do you need to do to address these fears and beliefs?

_____

_____

_____

_____

_____

_____

_____

_____

_____

_____

_____

_____

_____

101. How committed are you to continuing your planning, research, and action steps toward defining your passion and living it? How can you stay motivated and positive as you work toward it?

_____

_____

_____

_____

_____

_____

_____

_____

_____

_____

_____

_____

_____

_____

102. If you live to age 90, how many days do you have left to live? *(90 minus your current age times 365.)* How many of those days are you willing to live disliking your life, your work, your relationships, or yourself?

_____

_____

_____

_____

_____

_____

_____

_____

_____

_____

_____

_____

_____

Your Next Steps

Don't ask yourself what the world needs; ask yourself what makes you come alive. And then go and do that. Because what the world needs is people who have come alive.

Howard Thurman

Not too many years ago, I had an entirely different life. I was raising my children and trying to re-energize my long career in public relations. I was doing just what you are doing now—searching, trying to figure it out, taking workshops and courses, gathering information, and trying to decide what to do with it all.

Over the course of a few years, I changed my life entirely. I wasn't 100 percent sure I was on the right track when I went back to school to get a coaching certification, but all the signs seemed to point in that direction.

Coaching has led me to blogging, authoring multiple self-improvement books, and building a successful online business. I would never have dreamed my first tentative steps toward finding my passion would lead me here.

It seems like there's a huge chasm between having an inkling about what your passion might be and actually creating a passionate life. The only secret to crossing that chasm is action—doing something every day toward figuring it out and making it happen.

At first, those actions feel random and without purpose. But each action leads you forward to more clarity, inspiration, self-awareness, and knowledge about what you want for your life.

If you have followed this journal and completed the questions and prompts, then your actions are grounded in thorough preparation and self-knowledge. Take full advantage of everything you have learned about yourself as you make choices and decisions moving forward.

The next steps you might take include the following points.

- Reviewing all your responses and ideas and creating a master list of goals and action steps you need to take.
- Breaking those action steps into manageable chunks to fit the time you have available to work on them.
- Assigning actions to your calendar every week to keep the process moving.
- Setting up an accountability system to keep you on track.
- Regularly measuring your decisions and actions against your values to ensure you don't deviate from your values.

- Regularly communicating with anyone in your family who will be impacted by your decisions and life changes.
- Working to remain positive, motivated, and upbeat as you pursue your passion, even when you encounter setbacks.

Passion is a great motivator for learning things you previously would have never attempted. You'll discover how much you are actually capable of achieving when you are driven by passion. Once you are hooked by your passion, it will reel you in almost effortlessly.

When you find something that makes you come alive, you will be carried along by your own enthusiasm. You will be highly focused on something that puts you in a meditative flow of action.

This is the way it feels when athletes become intensely focused on their sports, when artists are emerged in their craft, when time and space disappear, and you are one with whatever you are doing.

As you pursue your passion, other opportunities and doors will open for you. Just as my coaching work led me to an online business, your passion can provide you with new and interesting ways of exploring and living it. Your love of sports could lead to a mentoring role with young athletes. Your desire to travel could transform you into a travel writer.

Once the floodgate of passion and enthusiasm is opened, you'll be carried away on a tidal wave of creative energy and possibilities.

It is very much like falling in love. All of your cares and worries fade into the background because you are filled with passion. Suddenly, all of the things you struggled with previously—the "what ifs" and "I don't know if this can work"—will fall away naturally or without much difficulty.

That's not to say there won't be problems to address. Challenges will always crop up. But they will no longer dominate your life and sour your mood.

Occasionally people find one passion and stick with it for life without deviating from it. But most of the time passion emerges slowly over time, and it evolves and shifts as you gain more experience and understanding.

Don't be disappointed if passion doesn't hit you over the head. It probably won't. But whether it happens like a thunderbolt or a slow transformation, the result is the same. You will be living a life of passion.

You will need to maintain your life passion by continuing to experiment and stretch yourself. Remain open to possibilities and opportunities and follow unknown paths where your passion might lead you.

Your life passion is not simply a destination—it's a life-long journey. Once you are on the passion path, you will never be satisfied with anything less.

❯ Want to Learn More? ❮

If you'd like to learn more about relationship skills, powerful questions, and other personal growth topics, please visit my blog at liveboldandbloom.com for more articles, or check out my online course offerings at liveboldandbloom.com/courses.

❯ Did You Like *The Life Passion Journal* ? ❮

Thank you so much for purchasing *The Life Passion Journal*. I'm honored by the trust you've placed in me and my work by choosing this journal to improve your life. I truly hope you've enjoyed it and found it useful.

I'd like to ask you for a small favor. Would you please take just a minute to leave a review for this book on Amazon? This feedback will help me continue to write the kind of books that will best serve you. If you really loved the journal, please let me know!

Skills Inventory

Physical Skills

Agility/quickness
Athleticism
Coordination
Outdoor skills
Stamina/endurance
Strength

Verbal/Written Skills

Clear communicator/business written
Clear communicator/creative written
Clear communicator/spoken
Defining
Editing/restatement
Interviewing
Persuading
Summarizing

Influencing/Motivational Skills

Builds teams and alliances
Negotiates agreements

Persuades and guides
Relates well to others
Sells ideas/promotes
Settles disagreements
Skills

Learning Skills

Analyzing/assessing
Extrapolates to other situations
Identifying trends
Learns by doing
Learns by listening
Learns by process in the moment
Learns by reading
Observation
Retains facts and details
Summarizing
Synthesizing

Leadership Skills

Accepts responsibility
Adapts to new situations

Builds teams
Delegates
Demonstrates integrity and values
Guides and coaches
Identifies direction
Identifies problems and solutions
Manages meetings/conferences
Manages self
Manage up and down the organization
Monitors progress
Motivates
Sets priorities
Works well independently
Works without supervision

Teaching/Coaching Skills

Advise/coach one on one
Create learning opportunities
Design learning modules
Encourage/guide
Facilitate group process
Identifying learning areas
Instruct/provide detail

Listening
Provide instruction/input
Summarize/provide overview

Doing/Hands-On Skills

Constructing
Cooking
Designing
Gardening
Handling
Installing
Operating tools/machines
Producing
Repairing/restoring

Administrative Skills

Anticipate problems
Assuring quality
Build alliances/teams
Computer literate
Delegate
Evaluating

Execution of projects
Follow-through
Forecasting
Operates under stress
Planning
Recommending
Responding
Scheduling
Setting goals/priorities

Artistic Skills

Creating/shaping things
Designing materials
Designing visually
Imagining
Improvising
Interrelating materials/themes
Noticing beauty/aesthetics
Performing
Symbolic thinking

Interpersonal Skills

Accepting

Forms good rapport
Handles problems/complaints
Helping
Listening
Mediating
Problem-solving
Providing service
Sympathetic

Innovative Skills

Adapting ideas
Creating
Demonstrating foresight
Developing new approaches
Experimenting
Imagining
Noticing trends
Tolerating lack of structure

Math/Financial Skills

Accounting
Budgeting
Estimating

Financial planning
Forecasting
Identifying trends
Math computation
Problem-solving
Using statistics

400 Value Words

Ability
Abundance
Acceptance
Accomplishment
Achievement
Acknowledgment
Adaptability
Adequacy
Adroitness
Adventure
Affection
Affluence
Alertness
Aliveness
Ambition
Amusement
Anticipation
Appreciation
Approachability
Artfulness

Articulacy
Assertiveness
Assurance
Attentiveness
Attractiveness
Audacity
Availability
Awareness
Awe
Balance
Beauty
Beingness
Belongingness
Benevolence
Blissfulness
Boldness
Bravery
Brilliance
Briskness
Buoyancy

Calmness
Camaraderie
Candor
Capability
Care
Carefulness
Certainty
Challenge
Charity
Charm
Chastity
Cheerfulness
Clarity
Classy
Cleanliness
Cleverness
Closeness
Cognizance
Comfort
Commitment

Compassion
Competence
Complacency
Completion
Composure
Concentration
Confidence
Conformity
Congruency
Connection
Consciousness
Consistency
Contentment
Continuity
Contribution
Control
Conviction
Conviviality
Coolness
Cooperation
Copiousness
Cordiality
Correctness
Courage

Courtesy
Craftiness
Creativity
Credibility
Cunning
Curiosity
Daring
Decisiveness
Decorum
Deepness
Deference
Delicacy
Delight
Dependability
Depth
Desire
Determination
Devotion
Devoutness
Dexterity
Dignity
Diligence
Diplomacy
Direction

Directness
Discernment
Discipline
Discovery
Discretion
Diversity
Dreaming
Drive
Duty
Dynamism
Eagerness
Economy
Ecstasy
Education
Effectiveness
Efficiency
Elation
Elegance
Empathy
Encouragement
Endurance
Energy
Enjoyment
Enlightenment

Entertainment	Fineness	Growth
Enthusiasm	Finesse	Guidance
Evolution	Firmness	Happiness
Exactness	Fitness	Harmony
Excellence	Flexibility	Health
Excitement	Flow	Heart
Exhilaration	Fluency	Helpfulness
Expectancy	Fluidity	Heroism
Expediency	Focus	Holiness
Experience	Fortitude	Honesty
Expertise	Frankness	Honor
Exploration	Freedom	Hopefulness
Expressiveness	Friendliness	Hospitality
Extravagance	Frugality	Humility
Extroversion	Fun	Humor
Exuberance	Gallantry	Hygiene
Facilitating	Generosity	Imagination
Fairness	Gentility	Impact
Faith	Genuineness	Impartiality
Fame	Giving	Impeccability
Fascination	Grace	Independence
Fashion	Gratefulness	Industry
Fearlessness	Gratitude	Ingenuity
Fidelity	Gregariousness	Inquisitiveness

Insightfulness	Logic	Originality
Inspiration	Longevity	Outlandishness
Instinctiveness	Love	Outrageousness
Integrity	Loyalty	Passion
Intelligence	Majesty	Peacefulness
Intensity	Mastery	Perceptiveness
Intimacy	Maturity	Perfection
Intrepidness	Meekness	Perseverance
Introversion	Mellowness	Persistence
Intuition	Meticulousness	Persuasiveness
Intuitiveness	Mindfulness	Philanthropy
Inventiveness	Moderation	Piety
Joy	Modesty	Playfulness
Judiciousness	Motivation	Pleasantness
Justice	Mysteriousness	Pleasure
Keenness	Neatness	Plentifulness
Kindness	Nerve	Poise
Knowledgeableness	Obedience	Polish
Lavishness	Open-mindedness	Popularity
Leadership	Openness	Potency
Learning	Optimism	Practicality
Liberation	Opulence	Pragmatism
Liberty	Order	Precision
Liveliness	Organization	Preeminence

Preparedness	Resolve	Sharing
Presence	Resourcefulness	Shrewdness
Privacy	Respect	Significance
Proactivity	Restfulness	Silence
Professionalism	Restraint	Silliness
Proficiency	Reverence	Simplicity
Prosperity	Richness	Sincerity
Prudence	Rigor	Skillfulness
Punctuality	Sacredness	Smartness
Purity	Sacrifice	Solidarity
Qualification	Sagacity	Solidity
Quickness	Saintliness	Solitude
Quietness	Sanguinity	Sophistication
Readiness	Satisfaction	Soundness
Realism	Security	Speed
Reason	Self-control	Spirit
Recognition	Selflessness	Spirituality
Recreation	Self-realization	Spontaneity
Refinement	Self-reliance	Stability
Reflection	Sensitivity	Stillness
Relaxation	Sensuality	Strength
Reliability	Serenity	Structure
Resilience	Service	Substantiality
Resolution	Sexuality	Success

Sufficiency
Superbness
Support
Supremacy
Surprise
Sympathy
Synergy
Tactfulness
Teamwork
Temperance
Thankfulness
Thoroughness
Thoughtfulness
Thrift
Tidiness
Timeliness

Traditionalism
Tranquility
Transcendence
Trust
Trustworthiness
Truth
Understanding
Uniqueness
Unity
Usefulness
Utility
Valor
Variety
Victory
Vigor
Virtue

Vision
Vitality
Vivacity
Warmth
Watchfulness
Wealth
Wholesomeness
Willfulness
Willingness
Winning
Wisdom
Wittiness
Wonder
Worthiness
Zeal
Zest
Zing